ADEL

Published by
Wise Publications
14-15 Berners Street, London W1T 3LJ, UK.

Exclusive distributors:
Music Sales Limited
Distribution Centre, Newmarket Road,
Bury St Edmunds, Suffolk IP33 3YB, UK.

Music Sales Pty Limited
120 Rothschild Avenue, Rosebery,
NSW 2018, Australia.

Order No. AM993729
ISBN: 978-1-84772-571-4
This book © Copyright 2008 Wise Publications,
a division of Music Sales Limited.

Edited by Fiona Bolton.
Arranged by Derek Jones, Daniel Goodger and Joe Davison.
Music processed by Paul Ewers Music Design.

Printed in the EU.

www.musicsales.com

ADELE *19*

Wise Publications
part of The Music Sales Group

London / New York / Paris / Sydney / Copenhagen / Berlin / Madrid / Tokyo

Best For Last

Words & Music by Adele Adkins

on now,___ I'm try - ing to tell you just___ how I'd like___ to hear the words___ roll out___

think that___ I know___ things may nev - er change.___ But I'm___ still

___ of your___ mouth fi - nal - ly. Say that it's al - ways___ been___ me that's made you

hop - ing one___ day I___ might hear you say... I make you

♩ = **80 a tempo**

D   Em   D/F♯   G

feel a way you've nev - er felt___ be - fore.___ And I'm

1° R.H. tacet till*

D   Em   D/F♯   G

all you need_____ and that you'd nev - er want___ more.___ Then

9

1.
Free time
N.C.

2. Why____ is it ev - 'ry - time I think I've tried____ my hard - est

it turns out it ain't e - nough? You're still not men - tion - ing____ love. What am

I sup - posed___ to do to make__ you want__ me prop - 'ly? I'm

2.
Free time
N.C.

But____ de - spite____ the truth that I know, I find____ it hard to

Daydreamer

Words & Music by Adele Adkins

Chasing Pavements

Words & Music by Adele Adkins & Francis White

Cold Shoulder

Words & Music by Adele Adkins.

Crazy For you

Words & Music by Adele Adkins.

Verse 5:
My, oh my, how my blood boils,
It's sweetest for you.
It strips me down bare
And gets me into my favourite mood.

Verse 6:
I keep on trying,
I'm fighting these feelings away.
But the more I do,
The crazier I turn into.

Melt my Heart To Stone

Words & Music by Adele Adkins & Francis White

First Love

Words & Music by Adele Adkins

Right As Rain

Words & Music by Adele Adkins, J Silverman & Leon Michels

Make You Feel My Love

Words & Music by Bob Dylan

to make you feel my love.

Tired

Words & Music by Adele Adkins & Francis White

tired.

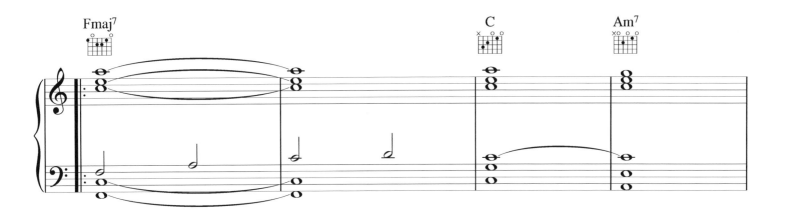

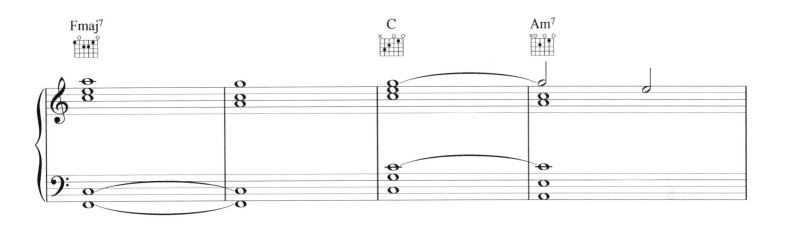

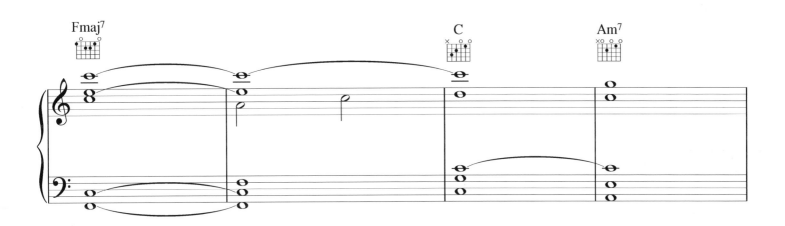

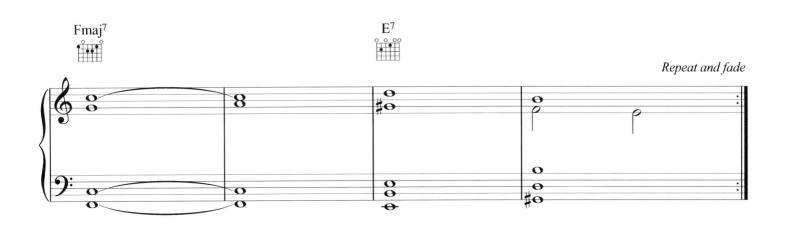

59

My Same

Words & Music by Adele Adkins

Hometown Glory

Words & Music by Adele Adkins

6789